Sweet Dreams Lullabies

Lyrics by Harris Tobias
Music by Keith Hopwood
Illustrations by Dubbo

ISBN: 978-1-943314-23-2

This book is dedicated to all the precious little ones, all the little sleepy heads. May their sleep be peaceful and their dreams be sweet.

A Father's Wish

Oh little one, my precious one
What ever will you be
When you are grown into a man
As grown up as me

Will you be a cobbler, a baker, a sweep?
Will you be a shepherd
And look after your sheep?

Will you be a rich man, a poor man, a lord?
Or will you be a soldier
And live by your sword?
Whatever you do, your father prays
May you be happy all of your days
May you be healthy
And may you be strong
May you live well
And may you live long

Will you be a husband, a father like me
Or will you be a sailor
And sail 'cross the sea
I hope that you marry
And have a fine wife
And you'll be a good man
And have a good life

A Father's Wish

words: Harris Tobias
music: Keith Hopwood

89bpm

Piano

Melody

Oh lit tle one my prec ious one

what ev er will you be when you are grown in to a

man as grown up as me Will you be a cob bler a ba ker or a

be a hus band a fa ther like me or will you

29

be a sai lor and sail cross the sea

I hope that you mar ry have a fine wife

and you'll be a good man and have a good life

You can hear these lullabies sung st:
https://soundcloud.com/horvis

Dream-ship Lullaby

Listen to the waves as they wash upon the beach
As your dream-ship hoists its anchor
And its sails are filled with sleep

The ship sets out to sea and leaves the shore behind
And we sail into the starry night to see what we can find
Goodbye old familiar things we sail into the new
May your dreams be filled with sunny skies
And may all those skies be blue

Go to sleep my little one, your fairy ship awaits
Her sails are made of silken gold and pirates are her mates
Her hold is filled with treasure and her masts are trees of ash
A hundred dolphins guide your way see them flash and splash

Listen to the waves as they roll in from the deep
As your dream-ship hoists its anchor
And its sails are filled with sleep

Your dream-ship floats upon the sea, a sea that's filled with fish
You're the dream-ship's captain and she'll sail where 'ere you wish
She'll sail through sunny waters and she'll sail through wind and storm
And she'll bring you safely back to me when the sky is pink with dawn

Listen to the waves as they wash upon the beach
As your dream-ship hoists its anchor
And its sails are filled with sleep

Dreamship Lullaby

words: Harris Tobias
music: Keith Hopwood

Piano

Melody

Lis ten to the waves as they

wash up on the beach as your dream ship hoists its an chor and its

sails are filled with sleep The ship sets out to sea and

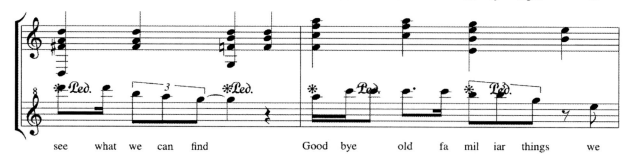

leaves the shore be hind and we sail in to the star ry night to

see what we can find Good bye old fa mil iar things we

1

2

sail in to the new   May your dreams be filled with sun ny skies and may

all those skies be blue   Go to sleep my lit tle one   your

fai ry ship a waits   her sails are made of sil ken gold and

pir ates are her mates   her hold is filled with trea sure   and her

masts are trees of ash   a hun dred dol phins guide your way

3

4

sail through sun ny wat ers and she'll sail through wind and storm and she'll

bring you safe ly back to me when the sky is pink with dawn

Listen to the waves as as they

wash up on the beach as your dream ship hoists its an chor and its sails

are filled with sleep

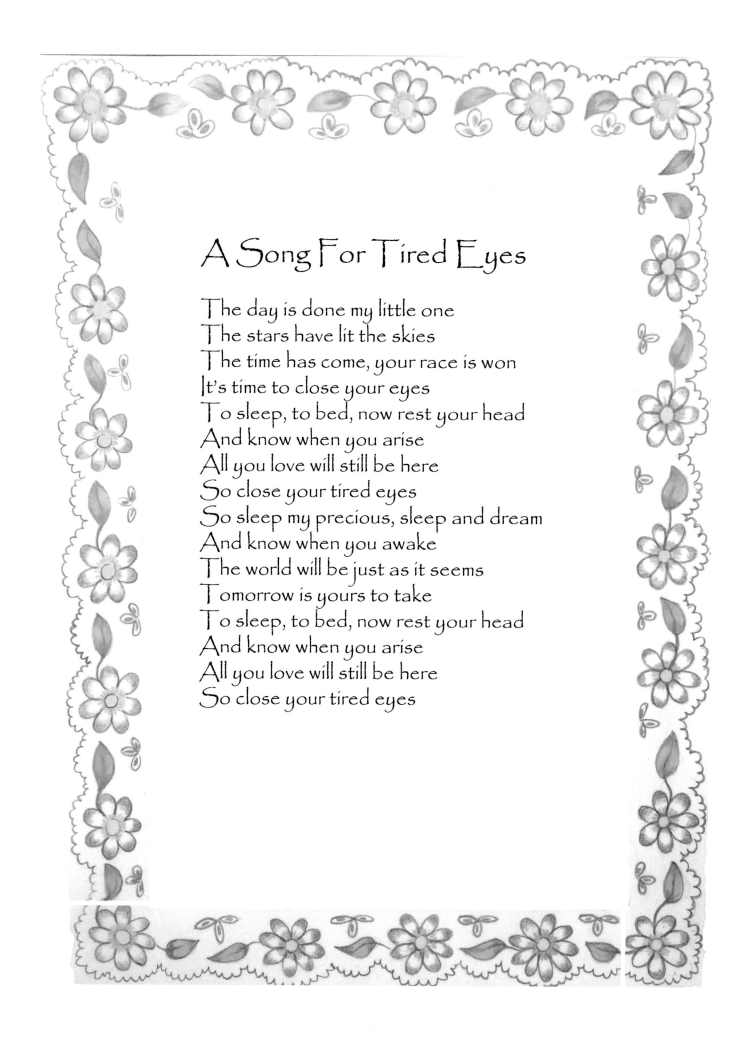

A Song For Tired Eyes

The day is done my little one
The stars have lit the skies
The time has come, your race is won
It's time to close your eyes
To sleep, to bed, now rest your head
And know when you arise
All you love will still be here
So close your tired eyes
So sleep my precious, sleep and dream
And know when you awake
The world will be just as it seems
Tomorrow is yours to take
To sleep, to bed, now rest your head
And know when you arise
All you love will still be here
So close your tired eyes

A Song For Tired Eyes

words: Harris Tobias
music: Keith Hopwood

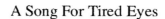

close your ti - red eyes

So sleep my

prec ious sleep and dream and know when you awake the

world will be just as it seems to mor row is

yours to take To sleep to bed now rest your

head and know when you arise all you

love will still be here so close your ti - red eyes

You can hear these lullabies sung st:
https://soundcloud.com/horvis

Magic Land

Hush sweet child and close your eyes
Momma's gonna sing you some lullabies
About a magic land I heard
Where a horse can fly just like a bird
Children ride them around the sun
Then home again when day is done
In this magic land you'll see
Unicorns running free
Where this land is no one knows
You can only see it when your eyes are closed
So go there now my little one
Ride your horse around the sun
Ride through fields on a unicorn
And tell me about it in the morn

Magic Land

words: Harris Tobias
music: Keith Hopwood

Hush sweet child and close your eyes

mom ma's gon na sing you some lul a bi es a bout a mag ic land I

heard Where a horse can fly just like a bird Chil dren

ride them round the sun then home a gain when day is done

In this mag ic land you'll see un i corns run ning free

Where this land is no one knows you can on ly see it when your eyes are closed

So go there now my lit tle one ride your horse a round the sun

Ride through fields on a u ni corn and tell me all a bout it in the morn

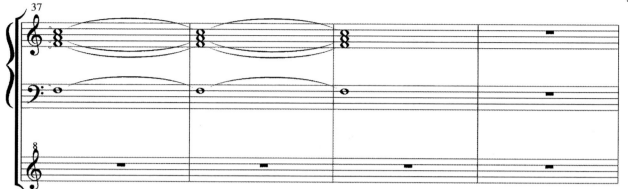

You can hear these lullabies sung st:
https://soundcloud.com/horvis

Mama Loves You

Hush little baby
Whatever you do
There's no need for crying
Your mama's not lying
Daddy's out buying
A new toy for you

It's time to stop fussing
This aint no discussion
It's time you were trustin'
All that we do
All that we do
We do it for you

So dry your tears
Shrug off your fears
Mama is here
And all will be well
Sleep and you'll grow
Up sound as a bell

So close your eyes
And silence your cries
Soon you'll realize
Your mama loves you
More than you know
More than she'll tell

Mama Loves You

bpm: 96

words: Harris Tobias
music: Keith Hopwood

Piano

Melody

Hush Lit tle bab y what

ev er you do   There's   no   need   for cry ing   your ma ma's   not   ly ing

Dad dy's out buy ing   a   new toy   for you   It's

2

time to stop fus sing this ain't no dis cus sion it's time you were trustin' all

that we do All that we do we do it for you So

dry your tears shrug off your fears ma ma is here and

all will be well Sleep and you'll grow up sound as a bell So

close your eyes and si lence your cries soon you'll re a lize your

ma ma loves you More than you know more than she'll tell

You can hear these lullabies sung st:
https://soundcloud.com/horvis

Sleep and Grow

Hush little baby don't you cry
Mama's gonna sing you a lullaby
I'll tell you a story you should hear
It'll make your sadness disappear

So dry your eyes and listen well
And hear this story I will tell
Once there was a little child
Just like you, so sweet and mild

Fat and dimpled just like you
She laughed and smiled the way you do
And as sure as there's a heaven above
This baby was most dearly loved

And when this little girl would cry
Her mom would sing this lullaby
This child is now all big and grown
And she has babies of her own
And how I know this story's true
I was that baby just like you

One day you'll wake and you'll be grown
And you'll have babies of your own
And you'll sing them lullabies
Until they close their tired eyes

Sleep and Grow

words by: Harris Tobias
music by: Keith Hopwood

2

Just like you so sweet and mild

Fat and dimp led just like you she laughed and smiled the way you do

As sure as there's a hea ven a bove This ba by was most dear ly loved

And when this lit tle girl would cry her mo ma would sing this lul a by This

child is now all big and grown and she has ba bies of her own

And how I know this sto ry's true I was that ba by just like

you One day you'll wake and you'll be grown

And you'll have ba bies of your own and you'll sing them

lull a bies un til they close their ti red eyes

4

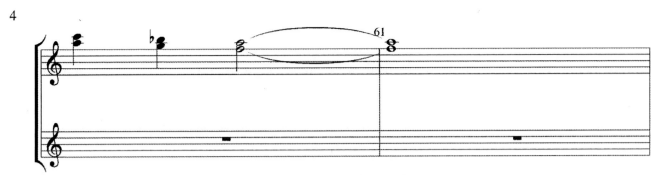

When You Awake

When you awake my little one
When you awake you'll see
How much fun we're gonna have
Bouncin' on mama's knee
Bouncing' bouncin' bouncin'
Bouncin' on mama's knee

When you awake sweet child
You'll see a brand new dawn
The sun will shine and the birds will sing
Happy that you were born
Happy, happy, happy
Happy that you were born

So close your eyes
And hush your cries
Tomorrow will be just fine
Dry your tears and face your fears
I'm so glad that you are mine
Happy, happy, happy
Happy that you are mine

When You Awake

words: Harris Tobias
music: Keith Hopwood

When you a wake my lit tle one when

you a wake you'll see how much fun we're gon na have

bouncin' on mom ma's knee boun cin' boun cin' boun cin'

bouncin' on mom ma's knee When

you a wake sweet child you'll see a brand new dawn

2

The sun will shine and the birds will sing   hap py that you were born

hap py hap py hap py   hap py that you were born   So

close your eyes and hush your cries   to morrow will be just fine

Dry your tears and face your fears   I'm so glad you are mine

hap py hap py hap py   hap py that you are mine

hap py   hap py   hap py   so hap py that you are   mine

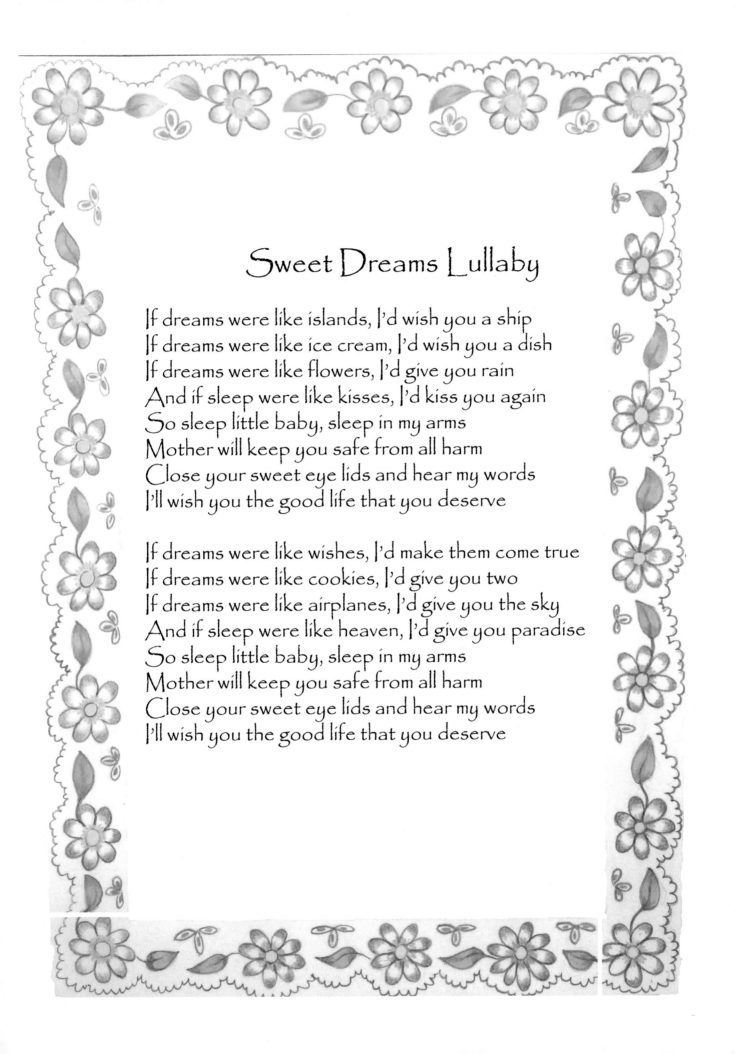

Sweet Dreams Lullaby

If dreams were like islands, I'd wish you a ship
If dreams were like ice cream, I'd wish you a dish
If dreams were like flowers, I'd give you rain
And if sleep were like kisses, I'd kiss you again
So sleep little baby, sleep in my arms
Mother will keep you safe from all harm
Close your sweet eye lids and hear my words
I'll wish you the good life that you deserve

If dreams were like wishes, I'd make them come true
If dreams were like cookies, I'd give you two
If dreams were like airplanes, I'd give you the sky
And if sleep were like heaven, I'd give you paradise
So sleep little baby, sleep in my arms
Mother will keep you safe from all harm
Close your sweet eye lids and hear my words
I'll wish you the good life that you deserve

Sweet Dreams Lullabye

words: Harris Tobias
music: Keith Hopwood

You can hear these lullabies sung st:
https://soundcloud.com/horvis

Other children's books by Harris Tobias that you might enjoy:

How The Cat Got Its Whiskers

The Adventures of MoonRivet

The Turtle's Ball

At The Robot Zoo

Five Little Froggies

The Adventures of Rocket Bob

The King's Dream

A Wish Too Far

The Broody Little Hen

The Big Fat Counting Book

The Three Chocolatiers

The Three Swords

The Wisdom of Yaqui the Bear

The Catch of the Day

The Contest

DragonSong

Square Sally in Circletown

How Birds Got Their Colors

The Amulet of Power

The Monkey & Elephant Fables

The Monkey & Elephant Book 1

DreamShip Lullaby

A Wish Too Far

A Child's Book of Riddles

A Chanukah Story

5 Children's Poems

A Prisoner of Beauty

The Stone Apples

Baker's Dozen

Bug Alphabet

Catch of the Day

Farm Song

Stinky Feet

How The Pelican Got Its Beak

How The Zebra Got Its Stripes

A Child's Book of Riddles

Snails, Scales & Animal Tales

Storyland Jack

The Three Brothers

Trumpet The Homeless Troll

And for older readers:

A Felony of Birds
The Greer Agency
Alien Fruit
Chronon, Time Travel Stories
Hold The Anchovies
Peaceful Intent
The Stang
Dick Danks, The Collected Stories
Assisted

All titles are available on
Amazon in print and as ebooks..
Just enter Harris Tobias in the search field.

Made in the USA
Lexington, KY
01 September 2018